Mel Did Not Say "Yum!"

by Liza Charlesworth

ISBN: 978-1-338-84424-5

Art Director: Tannaz Fassihi; Designer: Cynthia Ng; Illustrated by Kevin Zimmer
Copyright © Liza Charlesworth. All rights reserved. Published by Scholastic Inc.

3 4 5 6 7   68   26 25 24

Printed in Jiaxing, China. First printing, June 2022.

SCHOLASTIC

It is Mel.
Mel did not say "YUM!"

"I bet I can get Mel
to say YUM!" said Mom.

3

Mom got a big pot.

Mom put in a lot of mud.
Mud, mud!

Mom put in a lot of red jam.
Jam, jam!

Mom put in a lot of gum.
Gum, gum!

Mom put in a lot of rocks.
Rocks, rocks!

Mom put in a lot of socks.
Socks, socks!

Mom let the pot get hot.
Hot, hot!

Mom got Mel a bib.
Then, Mom fed him
a cup of mud.

Mel had a big sip. SIP!

What did Mel say?
"YUM, YUM, YUM!
YUM, YUM, YUM!"

Read & Review

Invite your learner to point to each short-vowel word and read it aloud.

Short e

Mel

bet

let

Short i

big

is

it

him

in

did

bib

sip

Short a

can
had   jam

Short u

cup
mud
yum
gum

Short e

get
red
fed

Short o

not   got   hot
lot
pot
mom
socks   rocks

Fun Fill-Ins

Read the sentences aloud, inviting your learner to complete them using the short-vowel words in the box.

Mel jam yum hot bib

1. This story is about Mom and _____.
2. Mom put in a lot of red _____!
3. Mom let the pot get _____.
4. Mel had to wear a _____.
5. At the end, Mel did say "_____!"